CREATIVE THINKING

Problem Solving Across the Curriculum

Ages 10-12

Activities and ideas to develop a creative perspective
in problem solving across the curriculum

Ann Baker

A & C Black • London

CONTENTS

Introduction 3

How to Use this Book 4

Teachers' File 5
About creative problem
solving 6
ICT Tips 9
Assessment 10
Parent involvement 10
PCM Notes 11

Quick Starts 13
Starter activities requiring
little or no preparation

Activity Bank 17
27 photocopiable activities

Mathematics
Jumping Fleas 18
Map It 19
Fraction Quilt Blocks 20
Popcorn Fundraiser 21
Going Somewhere? 22
Lost the Plan? 23

Visual Literacy
Cartoon Story Board 24
Dress That Flea 25
Comic Strip Conventions 26
Setting the Scene 27
Signs and Symbols
Everywhere 28
Missing Steps 29

Values
Don't Do It! 30
But I only told one friend 31
My Poor Dog 32
Reality TV 33
Show Off 34

Music and Dance
Farmyard Music 35
Sound Scape 36
Stress Buster Bustle 37
All Do the New Hokey Cokey 38

Communication
Wanted 39
Good Food Just Got Better 40
Guess What's in My Mind 41
Over to You, Channel 42 42
Rumbustical 43
The Perfect Character 44

Challenges

Task cards that draw together and consolidate skills, with clear step-by-step instructions. These tasks are ideal for challenging and extending older primary pupils (Year 6).

How to Have No Friends 46
Hum, Humming a Round 46
Hunters 47
Make a Scene 47
Picaria 48
Hook Your Audience 48

INTRODUCTION

Adults accept that problems will occur at home or at work, and that they need the disposition, skills and strategies to deal with them. Children need to be given opportunities to identify exactly what the presented problem is, and shown creative strategies to help them solve it and persist with challenging situations.

Creativity is at the heart of learning. Children are more resilient in their learning when they are absorbed, focused and challenged in the activities they undertake. Problem solving and investigations across the curriculum require a creative perspective, which involves all three of these personal attitudes to learning.

The activities in this book present a wide range of problematic situations for which there is more than one solution or more than one approach to the solution. In real life, problems are not usually neatly presented nor are the solutions immediately visible. When a potential solution is found, it needs to be evaluated to see if it is the best solution possible. Creative thinking illustrates a flexibility of thought, which allows us to consider a variety of approaches to a problem.

These activities will lay the foundation skills, strategies and disposition needed for children to become lifelong problem solvers and versatile learners.

ABOUT THIS BOOK

TEACHERS' FILE

The teachers' file offers advice on how to make the most of this book. It defines the different types of problems presented and how children can benefit from using them. It contains ideas for classroom organisation as well as background notes, ICT tips, assessment ideas and suggestions for parental involvement.

QUICK STARTS

This section offers activity and game ideas that help to promote a community of problem solvers and creative thinkers who will take a risk, come up with ideas, and develop problem solving strategies and the disposition to persevere. These activities require little or no preparation and can be used across various learning areas to complement existing lesson plans.

ACTIVITY BANK

The activity bank contains 27 photocopiable activities that cover creative thinking and problem solving skills relating to mathematics, visual literacy, music and dance, values and communication. The activities can be used in any order and can be used by children working individually or in groups.

CHALLENGES

These photocopiable task cards offer creative investigational challenges. They can be given to individual pupils or groups, and they can be used at any time and in any order. The tasks have the potential to become extended projects where pupils will share, present and develop a wide range of communication skills.

HOW TO USE THIS BOOK

QUICK STARTS

Feeling Blue?

Draw a happy scene such as a birthday party, you winning a race or buying a new CD. Make one or two copies of it. Colour one scene a mixture of blues– light blue, dark blue, even a blue-purple. Does the scene still look happy? Why is that? Colour one scene in reds. What mood does that give? What if you use only yellows and greens? What conclusions can be made about colour and mood?

Quick Starts are ideal warm-up activities for the beginning of a lesson. Each activity is intended to provide 10-15 minutes of group or whole class discussion. Reflect on the completed task with the children. Ask what they learned and whether there was anything that surprised them.

Example

'Feeling Blue?' (Page 16), is designed to promote discussion over how colour can represent mood, using different colours to illustrate happy or sad scenes. The use of colour in the work of famous artists such as Van Gogh can be used to illustrate how his mood was reflected in his painting during the sad, dark period of his life.

ACTIVITY BANK

These photocopiable activities can be used by individuals, groups or the whole class. They could provide the focus for a whole lesson. The activities will not in themselves achieve the objectives, but they will make children start to think about these often complex issues and strategies. Whilst some of the activities have a problem solving focus, they are all designed to encourage pupils to think creatively. By becoming flexible, versatile, open-minded learners, they will develop the skills to think more objectively and laterally in their investigations and in the solutions to problems.

Example

'But I only told one friend' (PCM 14, Page 31) explores the pupils' own personal values in considering the needs of others. They are asked to consider all aspects of telling a secret and the responsibility of keeping a secret. This could be extended to include a discussion on rumours, privacy and most importantly, trust.

CHALLENGES

These photocopiable activities are perfect for use in learning centres, in the school library or in the classroom. The investigational nature of the activities is in line with National Curriculum requirements and supports the development of investigational problem-solving skills.

Example

'Hunters' (Task Card 3, page 47) develops pupils' observational skills. Apart from exploring everyday objects in close up through a magnifying glass, this task provides opportunities to investigate the detail of minibeasts, such as ants and spiders, as well as the structures of plants, in particular seed heads, flower heads, leaves and stems.

TEACHERS' FILE

BACKGROUND NOTES

Planning for creative thinking

Pupils at this level often don't want to take risks or to present in front of the class. By using open-ended problems and creating a strong sense of learning community, they will:

- take a risk and think creatively with minimum focus on the right answer (as often there isn't one)
- offer ideas to their peers, and listen and accept their peers' ideas without judgement
- think critically and reflect on ideas and strategies they and others use, to become skilful and strategic problem solvers (a journal would be useful)
- consider the contributions they make to a group
- participate fully in discussions and presentations
- become responsible and reciprocal learners.

Characteristics of the problems

There are five different types of problems presented in this book:

- Mathematical problems—focus on using estimation, efficient number strategies, shape and position with flexibility and strategic thinking.
- Visual literacy problems—focus on using elements of visual language (colour, position, shape and planning) to convey ideas, create mood and develop visual flexibility and creativity.
- Music and dance problems—focus on developing perceptions about the ways in which rhythm, pattern, sound and movement can be combined to create solutions to musical challenges.
- Values problems—focus on reflecting and evaluating responses to everyday problem situations where interpersonal or ethical decisions need to be made. They provide an opportunity for philosophical thinking.
- Communication problems—focus on communicating clearly through spoken and written language specific to the task, purpose and audience.

CLASSROOM ORGANISATION

Building creative thinking into the week

Pupils in the upper years can become disconnected from school activities. The problems in this book are topical and of interest to this age group. Through the open-ended problems pupils can bring their own experiences and interests to solving and presenting solutions. Fun is central to the activities but academic perseverance is also required. The pupils will become engaged in critical, creative, reflective and empathetic thinking which will enhance the weekly programme. The problems can be stand-alone, the focus of specific curriculum areas or integrated within the existing weekly plan.

Communication problems–focus on pupils getting their ideas across in a number of different ways and this will blend into many curriculum areas.

Visual Literacy problems–focus on art appreciation and critical literacy, integrating effectively into literacy or critical literacy lessons and media or art lessons.

Mathematics problems–complement the normal maths programme.

Values problems–reflect typical pupil issues that may arise in the week or are seen in youth culture or current world issues.

Music, Dance and **Visual Literacy** problems–integrate and blend easily into the weekly programme.

Equipment

Consideration has been given to ensuring that any equipment needed will be either readily available cheaply or can be gathered from recycling everyday objects and materials.

Try to ensure that pupils have access to:
- paper
- scissors
- plenty of coloured crayons or felt pens for the visual literacy activities
- 15 cm squares (plastic or card for drawing around) or 15 cm white paper squares ready cut
- scrap materials for noise making

Learning styles

We all use a variety of audio, visual and kinaesthetic approaches to support our learning. This book covers a broad range of learning styles. Pupils will respond verbally, mathematically, visually, dramatically and musically to the problems. They will need to think logically and systematically and respond creatively and flexibly, to solve problems and make their presentations. They will also be reflective and philosophical, and can respond kinaesthetically to act out and construct solutions. Most of the intelligences identified by Howard Gardner are addressed through the activities, for instance, when solving:

mathematical problems – pupils will interpret verbal and visual information, estimate, explain, represent, justify and present solutions

visual literacy problems – pupils will interpret and respond to visual and design elements, emotionally, critically and creatively through a range of media

music and dance problems – pupils will use rhyme, rhythm, tone and mood to interpret and create new forms of music and choreography

values problems – pupils will listen carefully, be empathetic and consider others' perspectives, before responding visually or verbally

communication problems – pupils will generate ideas and consider audience and purpose as they get those ideas across.

As the pupils work on and present their solutions they will be simultaneously using several intelligences or learning styles. This reflects the real world where one intelligence is rarely used in total isolation from the others.

Planning activities

Pupils need to be given time, space and encouragement to persist when the going gets tough, to retrace their steps or try a different tack. They need to know there is enough time to work through what seems a mess, organise themselves or break a task into small manageable steps. They also need the benefit of working with peers.

When planning the weekly schedule, allocate time, space and technologies required for the problem solving, and for the practice and presentation of solutions. You may need to include specific mini-lessons on problem solving strategies such as Polya's model, explained here:

See: What is this problem about? What is it asking me to do? What information am I given/do I need?

Plan: How can I get started? How can I make this manageable? What have I done like this before?

Do: This is how I actually collect, analyse, interpret and represent information and strategies for critical and creative thinking.

Check: How effective were we? What will we do next time?

CLASSROOM ORGANISATION

Presenting

Giving and watching presentations are an important feature of the problems in this book, so you may need to:

- negotiate and agree on rules for watching and listening to presentations and giving positive feedback
- review and extend strategies for getting and holding audience attention
- review multi-media options that can be used (props, visual images, sound effects, digital technologies)
- discuss timelines and expectations for presentations
- set acceptable parameters for choreography and words for songs
- encourage all pupils to find a way of contributing to the group presentations (even if it is simply making props).

Sharing and reflecting

To be successful open-ended problem solvers and presenters, pupils need a safe and supportive classroom space where they can be a community of learners who feel confident taking risks, make mistakes and feel supported by peers. The following questions will assist you to create such an environment:

- Is the classroom set-up comfortable for group work?
- Will the pupils have a choice of who they work with?
- Can Socratic circles be easily set up for open forums or discussions?
- Are the resources ready and accessible?
- Is there a space where products can be displayed?
- Are there displays showing strategies for group work, active listening and quality presentations?
- Is there room for pupils to move around?
- Is there a quiet area?

Creative thinking strategies

Many upper primary pupils are experienced with right answer only type questions and not open-ended problems. Suddenly being asked to be creative and take a risk could be difficult for them. Pupils at this age may become embarrassed when asked to do musical or dance presentations. You may need to model or scaffold various stages of the problem solving and presentation, and offer support as pupils:

- discover there is no exact prescription or right solution for the problem
- feel frustrated not knowing how to start or what to do
- run out of strategies to apply to the situations
- get stuck using a guess and check approach that 'fails' and don't know how to use information they've gathered
- try to make sense of the strategies, approaches and ideas of others
- learn about cooperation
- plan and rehearse a presentation.

General

There are many ways in which technology can be used to accompany the actual problem solving and to present and record performances. As the pupils work, there will be scope to use drawing programs to scan images into Word documents and capture photographic images as accompaniments to the solutions requiring procedures. Audio recorders and video cameras can be used as a part of the Music and Dance solutions. The actual performances can be recorded for reflection and later evaluation.

Video and Audio Equipment

Schools often have video cameras and digital cameras and audio recorders. Many of the problems presented in this book offer opportunities to capture pupil activity and performances. Parents can be invited to view segments at a special event. Pupils can become directors and mini movie-makers capturing each other's presentations. Editing packages such as Photo Simple make it easy to cut and overlay, images and sounds.

Interactive Whiteboards

If you are fortunate enough to have access to an interactive whiteboard, you will be able to demonstrate to the whole class how some of the software listed above can be used. You can also use it to show pre-recorded presentations, to freeze-frame and take closer looks at aspects of them. You can scan and present items of pupil work to involve the class in feedback and annotations on the work.

Software

There are many software packages that can be introduced and used effectively by pupils in the upper primary years.

Kid Pix provides a drawing program and a stamp facility that can enhance the problem solving in many ways. The stamp facility for instance would allow pupils to create their own versions of the 'blocks of land'. The ability to quickly draw lines enables pupils to create their own game boards and the free drawing facility has possibilities for many of the problems presented. Pupils with fine motor difficulties benefit from using these programs when problem solving.

Thinking With Pictures is an excellent mind mapping software package that can be used as part of brainstorming at the beginning of the problem solving process, as well as in problems that ask pupils to brainstorm ideas. The program can also be used to enhance the thinking and writing involved in communication problems.

Photo Simple is a very easy to use software program that allows digital photos to be manipulated at the click or drag of the mouse. Photo Simple comes with its own built-in wizard that guides you step-by-step through every process as the photo story is created. It is possible to zoom in, zoom out, take a different perspective and create stories, sequences or procedures as in 'how to draw a dog' and add voice overs or music backing.

PowerPoint, Paint programs and Word programs can all be used in conjunction with the problem solving to present solutions in a variety of formats.

Excel allows pupils to make graphs and present them in a number of different formats. This program could be used instead of emoticons for the graphing activity.

Interactive whiteboards come with their own software such as Smart Ideas and the Smart Notebook. These can also be used effectively to present solutions.

ASSESSMENT

Pupil assessment

As the pupils solve problems, it is possible to observe and record the strategies that they use. Some pupils will always stick to one approach, whereas others will try a variety of approaches. This gives you information not just about which strategies pupils use and how effectively they use them, but also information about how willing they are to take a risk and how flexibly they think.

Problem solving and creative thinking allows insights into pupil disposition, that is, how readily they begin thinking about the problem, how persistent they are in the face of a challenge and whether they have solving strategies. They may also favour a learning style they have a particular interest or talent in.

The different types of problems will also allow you to observe pupils as they work in a particular domain and to annotate work samples. The maths problems, for instance, allow mathematical information to be gained, such as: how reasonable their estimates are; what information they use to make them; and, what counting strategies they use to check their estimates. In the same way the other four types of problems will allow you to gain specific information related to the domain.

As the pupils work, you will be able to observe and note skills in:

- interpreting information
- drawing skills and effective use of colour and position
- working cooperatively with others to achieve a joint goal
- rhythm and tempo
- flexibility and stamina when performing dance sequences
- empathising with others
- and problem solving strategies and skills (of course).

Peer assessment

There will be many opportunities to engage in presenting and sharing, and peer assessment will be a part of the process. Encourage positive feedback where the pupils identify that a part of the presentation or product was particularly effective or clever. Only after several positive comments should any constructive criticism be given. Model possible sentence starters for the constructive criticism so that feedback is in the form of 'I would have liked to have heard some more about why you think peer pressure is such a strong influence' rather than 'You didn't explain...'

Self-assessment

At each reflection, focus on one aspect such as:
- cooperation
- persistence
- product
- strategies; ask the pupils to think about what they did well or found easy, and what they didn't do so well or found hard. Encourage the pupils to take responsibility for thinking about ways in which they might improve for next time.

PARENT INVOLVEMENT

Explain to parents that the pupils will work on open-ended problems requiring them to find solutions and create presentations. The goal is to link this to real-life problems that adults deal with each day. Ask parents to involve their children in some problem solving situations, for example, how to schedule the weekend's events that have set times and durations, and some of which overlap. This type of problem demonstrates skills in organisation and planning, sharing the workload and responsibility so that everything gets done smoothly and on time.

Invite parents to celebrate the success of their children as problem solvers and creative thinkers by coming to presentations of solutions, products and performances.

PCM NOTES

PCM 1 Allow time for the pupils to work out what a jump 50 times the height of the flea looks like, before asking them why the dog isn't worried. The pupils can then identify a landing spot and say how many times its own height the flea would have to jump to land on it. If the pupils have not thought about using a ruler, you might want to ask how using a ruler would help work out answers to the questions.

PCM 2 Review the map features, compass points and coordinates, as well as terms such as bay, north and west before the pupils begin to answer the questions on the page. Model questions that will help to eliminate large areas of the map to prepare the pupils for the treasure coordinates game. Good questions could include:

'Is it in the northern half of the map?'
'Is it along the C coordinate?'

PCM 3 Provide 15 cm squares or ask the pupils to make them. Allow time for the pupils to follow the rules for creating the first quilt block, before they try to work out the rules for the second. You may need to demonstrate how to measure the square and work out what a third of the side is, before the pupils have a go at testing the rule they have created for the second block. The pupils can then create their own quilt blocks.

PCM 4 Review strategies for multiplying money amounts by 10 and for making whole pound (£) amounts by multiplying 25 by 4, before the pupils work on the questions. Review strategies used for each question, before moving on to the next question. Encourage the pupils to pose questions that will foster strategic thinking.

PCM 5 The information given suggests that the man is going fishing. Ask the pupils to record the details that should be visible on the thermometer, clock, scales and petrol gauge. Look at coastal tide times on the internet so that estimates of tide times can be made. Ask the pupils to think about temperatures and weather conditions at different times of the day during the month of June.

PCM 6 This is a typical Fermi problem where the pupils will need to decide how to find out or on what basis to estimate the length and width of an average car. Allow time for this to happen before the pupils begin to design their car park layout.

PCM 7 Discuss the story-line and decisions about shots as shown on the story board, before asking the pupils to think about how the colour might change in each shot to show the changing situation. The pupils can then create and label a story board of their own.

PCM 8 Tell the pupils how difficult and fiddly it would have been to dress a flea. A web search locates two fleas dressed for their wedding. Ask the pupils to choose an event and to dress the fleas for that event. Encourage the pupils to include as much detail as possible and to add accessories such as earrings, bandaids or footballs to match the costume.

PCM 9 Ask the pupils to brainstorm comic strip conventions that they have seen, before they use them in comic strips they will create. Review the types of shots and views that can be used before they try to get their ideas across in visual form.

PCM 10 Discuss the position of the sun at different times of the day and what happens to shadows as the sun's position changes (take the pupils outside a few times during the day if necessary). The pupils can then complete the first scene and begin one of their own. Allow time for the pupils to discuss differences in ideas and reasons for them, before they add colour and details to the second scene.

PCM 11 Discuss the role of signs and the way that they convey a lot of meaning through very simple shapes and images, usually with no words or numbers at all. The pupils can then invent signs for the ideas presented on the page. Share some of the pupils' ideas, before they go on to invent their own situations and matching signs.

PCM 12 Illustrators begin a drawing by creating the basic shapes and proportions before they finetune and add details. Discuss this strategy with the pupils and let them practise on scrap paper, before they work on the actual examples on the page.

PCM 13 Allow time for the pupils to discuss the situation presented and what they believe is right and wrong behaviour. Talk about peer pressure situations that they have experienced, before they begin working on a scenario of their own. Share and discuss (philosophise about) some of the situations the pupils present to the class.

PCM NOTES

PCM 14 The page shows that when a secret is shared, it may be passed on to others and it may also be exaggerated and changed to become totally untrue. Ask the pupils to consider all aspects of telling a secret in the first place and the responsibility of keeping a secret.

PCM 15 Identify the difference between objective and subjective thinking, before the pupils discuss the pros and cons of having a dog put to sleep. Often when considering a situation such as this, insufficient time is spent identifying all aspects of the situation. The pupils may really have to think deeply to come up with reasons and arguments but they can do it with encouragement.

PCM 16 The issue about whether we can actually learn anything about relationships from watching reality TV is an important one. Allow time for the pupils to identify some issues presented recently on a reality show, before completing the page. Ask them to discuss whether the issues were dealt with effectively or not on the reality show. Use the presented ideas for further discussion.

PCM 17 Ask the pupils to discuss whether it is ever okay to show off, before giving them the page for discussion. Explain that it is quite common to keep a personal 'brag book' in which goals, steps to reach their goals and achievements are recorded. Ask the pupils to identify one thing that they have become successful at as a result of their own efforts.

PCM 18 If possible, play one or two country and western type songs. Draw attention to the repeating chorus line/s and the story-line of country songs, before the pupils create their own. Insist that the pupils write their songs with notations for the rhythm and animal noises, so that the whole class can join in.

PCM 19 Point out that the cartoon character is translating the sentence into sound effects that will get the message across. Explain that a sound scape tells a story without words. The pupils are to translate the story on the page into a sound scape that they will record and present to the class.

PCM 20 Have fun singing and creating words and movements to match the tune 'Wheels on the Bus', before asking the pupils to select a song and innovate on it to invent a stress buster dance. Allow time for evaluation of the tune selected, as well as the words and actions created.

PCM 21 Dances such as the 'Hokey Cokey' have survived many generations and still provide fun and exercise today Innovate on the 'Hokey Cokey', before asking the pupils to create a 21st century version that young people today would enjoy.

PCM 22 Review the meaning of 'compound words' and then present the wanted poster, explaining how broad the first clues are and how many words would fit them. Contrast this with the increasing specific details that limit the possibilities. The pupils can then create their own clues for their chosen compound words.

PCM 23 Start by showing the pupils some menu descriptors and alternative ways of presenting meals, if possible. The pupils will then be looking at ways basic meals can be redescribed and visually presented to make them look more appealing and expensive. The pupils can then revamp and rename other meals of their own.

PCM 24 Review the rules for active listening before playing 'Chinese Whispers'. Brainstorm reasons for messages changing as they are retold. Ask the pupils to use their information and ideas to plan a message, and guess what changes might happen to it during a game of 'Chinese Whispers'.

PCM 25 Review/watch an on-the-scene report before brainstorming what is going on in the scene presented. The pupils then work with a partner to create an interview, using the format provided. Allow time for a rehearsal before presentation.

PCM 26 The letters in the word 'rumbustical' are numbered consecutively to create a code. When writing a message, each letter in the word is given a matching number, and letters not in the word remain unchanged. This same code-making rule can be used with other long words where no letter is repeated.

PCM 27 Talk about the fact that we all would like a feature that we don't have, or wish that we could change something about ourselves. The pupils can then draw their own characters and add a speech or thought bubble showing what feature each character would like to change. They can then show what pairs of characters think of each other. Use the comments as the basis of a class reflection.

QUICK STARTS

Flick It

Pupils make a small 'flea' by screwing up a piece of paper. They then predict which finger they can flip it furthest with. They need to make a mark to flick from and predict the distance for each finger flick.

- A flea can jump fifty times its own height. Pupils can predict how many times the height of the 'flea' they can flick.
- An obstacle course and scoring strategy for flea flicks could be fun.

Classroom Walk About

Pairs of pupils work together for this activity. One person secretly writes the name of a spot or object in the classroom and then gives instructions for their partner to get to the chosen spot. Instructions can include position and location terms such as: number of paces, north, south, east, west, left and right or 180 degree turn.

The process is repeated taking turns to follow and to give instructions. Partners should discuss the strengths and weaknesses of instructions and aim for improvement with practice.

Guess my Quilt Block

Use the completed quilt blocks from PCM 3 to play 'Guess my Quilt Block'.

Select a quilt block and encourage the pupils to ask questions to find out which one you have selected. Questions should eliminate some of the quilt blocks each time until there is only one block left. Questions could include fraction and shape terms. For instance:

'Does you quilt block include any half way points?'
'Does your quilt block have any triangles in it?'

The pupils can play the game in pairs or small groups once the rules are established.

In the Style Of...?

Brainstorm a list of known songs and a list of music types (opera, rap, rock'n'roll) familiar to the class. Use these as musical challenges where the class is given a song and a music style and time to sing the song in the style of the given music. Allow time for actions to be added.

Measurement Brainstorms

Select a picture or stimulus. Ask the pupils to work in groups to brainstorm as many different types of measurement related to it as possible and to say the units and name the tools that are used for them. Using a car as a stimulus could result in a list including, kilometres, speed gauge, temperature, degrees, thermometer, petrol gauge, litres, tyre pressure, and engine size. Share the lists and talk about the importance of each type of measurement.

Kung Fu Line Dancing

Demonstrate or show a line dancing clip to the pupils. Have a class line dance practice. Do the same for some Kung Fu moves and then ask the pupils to work in groups to create a Kung Fu line dance. Ask them to record the steps and actions and to give them names so that when the music they select plays, they can call the steps and actions for their Kung Fu line dance as the class performs it.

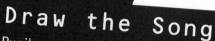

Draw the Song

Pupils work in groups to play 'draw the song'. The game is rather like 'Pictionary' but in this case the pupils have to think of a song title and draw a picture of it so that the rest of their group can guess what it is. They may include a drawing of the band or artist if they need to. Set a time limit so that the group who have correctly guessed most songs in a ten-minute period score points.

Adjectival Strings

Explain and demonstrate the rules for adjectival strings as follows. An adjectival string is a list of adjectives where every adjective begins with the last letter of the word that went before it. A string must always begin with an adjective starting with 'A' and no adjective can be repeated in the string. An example string could be; adorable, elegant, terrific, colourful, luscious. It is fun to make this into a 'round-the-world' type of game where all pupils stand. If on their turn they cannot think of a word or the word breaks the rules then the player sits down. The last player standing is the winner.

Homonym Doubles

For this activity the pupils create sentences that include a given homonym pair. An example would be:
'I paid my bus fare as I went to the fair.'
Insist on correct spelling of the homonyms or homophones.

Set criteria and create a team competition, for instance, the shortest/ longest, most creative, most interesting, or most amusing sentence scores a point for the team.

Prove Your Point

For this activity pupils are asked to answer questions about characters from real life, fiction, or well-know TV series or movies. A suitable question could be:
'What does the Queen have for breakfast?'
Pupils are asked to give an answer and justification for it. Answers can be serious or humorous, for example:
'The Queen has "Special K" because she is a very special person.'
Reflect on the answers and consider the justification for each answer to the question.

I Love that Cake

Pupils in small groups create a skit that shows a range of implications about the following scenario. A friend brought you a home-made cake and you said you loved it. In fact you hated it. Now every time the friend visits, they bring another cake. What should you do? The skit should show possible alternatives to the problem and the repercussions likely to flow on from each alternative.

'Tech' Talk

Talking about computers and computer parts and programs requires the use of words that didn't even exist twenty or so years ago. Some words now have completely different meanings or applications. A mouse for instance can refer to a creature or to the tool used for navigating on screen. Navigating—now that's an interesting word; it once meant to find a route in the real world but now we can find a route in cyber space, another new term. Brainstorm some 'tech' terms and try defining or illustrating them. Have fun, be creative and humorous.

Story Telling Prompts

Groups of four pupils select pictures from magazines that will be used by another group as the basis of a story. Into a bag go pictures of two or more characters, a setting (e.g. kitchen, beach, forest) and six objects (e.g. clothes, equipment, cars).

The bags will be swapped between the groups who may not open them until you have stated a genre for the narratives. Select from genres familiar to the pupils. Science fiction, suspense, fantasy, folk tales and legends are a sample that might appeal. Allow two or three minutes for each group to look at and sort the pictures into a sequence for their narrative. The pupils then tell the story to match the genre, one sentence each until all of the prompts have been used.

Feeling Blue?

Draw a happy scene such as a birthday party, you winning a race or buying a new CD. Make one or two copies of it. Colour one scene a mixture of blues—light blue, dark blue, even a blue-purple. Does the scene still look happy? Why is that? Colour one scene in reds. What mood does that give? What if you use only yellows and greens? What conclusions can be made about colour and mood?

Snakes Get a Bad Rap?

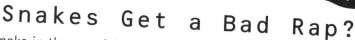

'Snake in the grass', 'speak with forked tongue' are terms used to describe the actions of people. They imply that snakes are all bad. Brainstorm some other 'snake' expressions. Do they all give snakes a bad rap? Why do you think the snake is used to represent things that are bad or evil? Think of some other animals and expressions about them. Which animals get a good/bad rap? Why is that?

ACTIVITY
BANK

NAME

Jumping fleas

I'm not worried, even if the flea does jump. He jumps 50 times his own height.

I can jump 50 times my own height. Where shall I aim for?

Watch out, here I come!

Why isn't the dog worried?

_____

_____

Where do you think the flea will land? _____

If the flea decided to jump in the dog's ear, how many times his own height would he have to jump?

_____

Draw some things that the flea could land on. Say how many times its own height the flea would have to jump.

Mathematics: *using measurement and proportion to estimate.*

NAME

Map It

The parrot is hiding in the north of the island, west of the Crow's Nest Mountains, but not in the bay. Where might the parrot be? _____

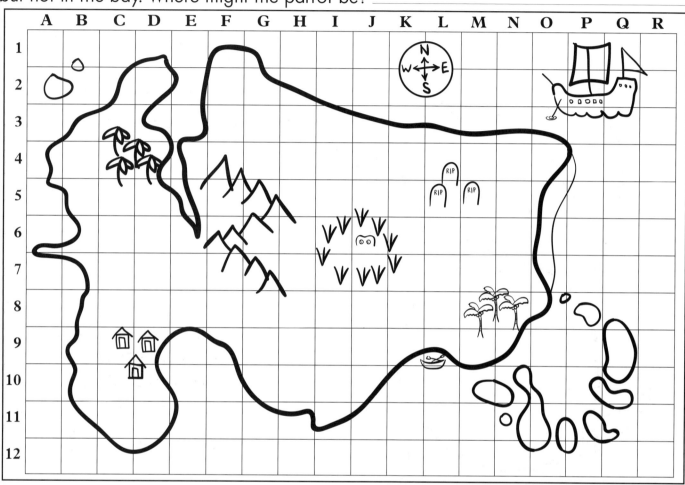

Where would you hide a golden fish? _____

Write some clues and see if your friend can locate it.

_____

_____

Where would you hide your treasure of silver? _____ Why? _____

_____

Ask a partner to ask you location and position questions to find it.

How effective were the questions?

_____

Make up a coordinates treasure game. Write the rules and ask a partner to play.

Mathematics: *location and position on a map.*

NAME

Fraction Quilt Blocks

The beginning rules for this quilt block were:

Mark a point halfway along each side of the square.

Join them to create a diamond.

Mark a point at the halfway mark on each side of the diamond.

Join them to create a square. Complete the rules.

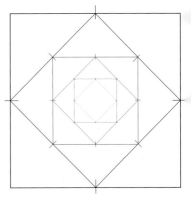

_____

_____

What do you think the rule for this quilt block was?

_____

_____

Make up two quilt blocks of your own.

Write the beginning rules for your quilt blocks.

Draw and colour your favourite quilt block. Use a square piece of paper with a 15 cm side. Your class can then make a fraction quilt using everyone's designs.

Mathematics: _using shapes and fractions._

NAME

Popcorn Fundraiser

If they sold all the popcorn, how much money would they take? _____

If they made an exact whole pound (£) amount in the first 10 minutes, what containers of popcorn might they have sold? Explain your thinking.

_____

_____

_____

If they want to take at least £50, what mix of packets do they need to sell? Show your strategies for working this out.

_____

_____

_____

Write some more questions for this scene. Work out the answers and then try the questions out on the class.

_____

_____

_____

_____

Mathematics: *strategies for working with money.*

NAME

Going Somewhere?

What is the man in this picture planning on doing?

_____

_____

_____

What is each of the objects for and what do they do?

_____

_____

_____

You will notice that all dates, times, temperatures and so on have been left off. If it is 6 o'clock on a Sunday morning in June, what should the missing information be?

_____

_____

_____

Create a page for a different hobby and see if a partner can add the missing information to it.

Mathematics: _using scales and measurement._

NAME

Lost the Plan?

The line painter has lost the car park map.

Now he's in trouble because he has got to make the road wide enough for two cars to pass each other. There must be spaces for all types of vehicles to park (not lorries and buses of course).

Where should the road go and where should the lines for the parking bays be painted so that the maximum number of cars can be parked?

Mark the roads and parking bays on the plan.

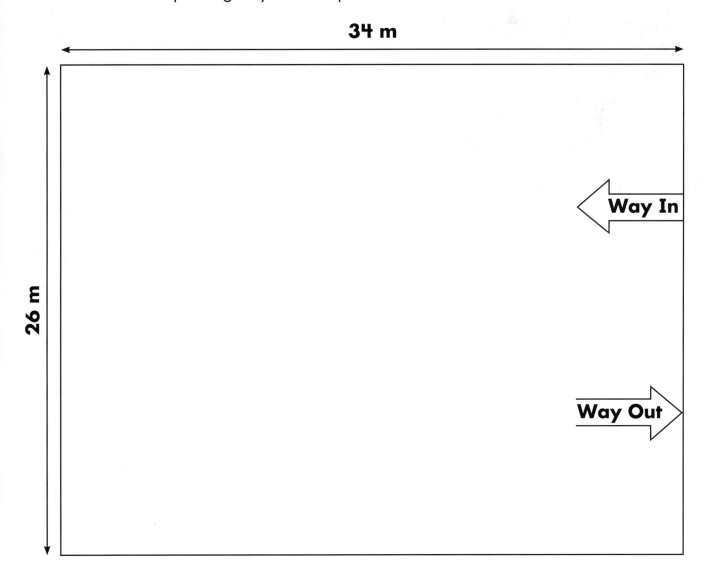

Compare with a friend's. How are they the same? Would they both work equally well?

What modifications would you make now? Why?

Mathematics: *exploring spatial and measurement applications.*

NAME

Cartoon Story Board

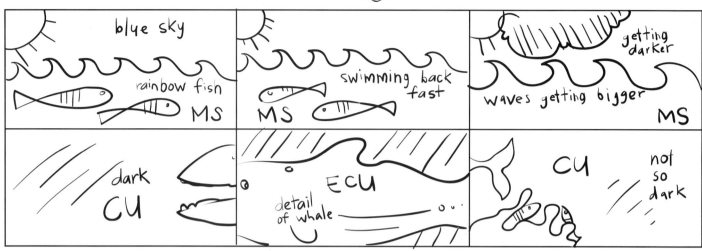

Look at the mix of quick drawings, words and camera shots used to create a story board for a cartoon. Add colour to help get the story across.

MS = mid shot

CU = close up

ECU = extreme close up

Make a story board for a cartoon of your own. Show quick sketch ideas, words and camera shots. Then add colour to help express the meaning.

Visual Literacy: *creating a story through images, colour and camera shots.*

NAME

DRESS THAT FLEA

The Victorians really did dress fleas. But they didn't dress them in clothes like we wear today. How would you dress this flea?

I hope they dress me in sports gear because I can jump really high.

Where could the flea go dressed like that?

_____

_____

What activities could a flea do in this outfit?

_____

_____

Visual Literacy: *creating an outfit to match a situation.*

NAME

Comic Strip Conventions

All comic strips use special conventions to create mood or movement in a cartoon.

List or show the conventions you have seen.

Create a cartoon to show each of these scenes:

A race

Romance

A surprise or new idea

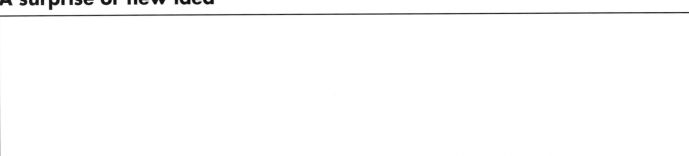

Visual Literacy: *creating mood and action through comic conventions.*

NAME

Setting the Scene

Add more detail to this scene. Decide on a time of day and use colour and shadow to show it. Hint at what might happen next in this scene.

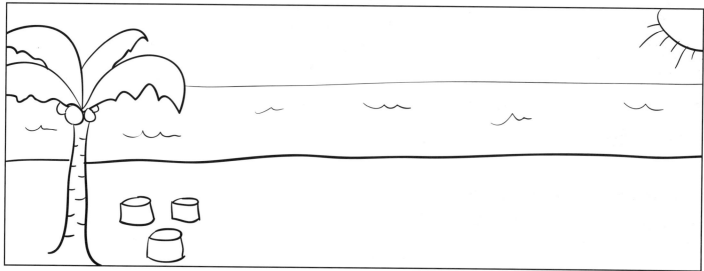

Start a scene of your own. Ask your friends what they think the scene is of and what time of day it is from the clues you have shown. Ask them to predict what they think might happen next in your scene.

Do your friends all have the same ideas about your scene? Give reasons for this.

Visual Literacy: *using colour to create time and mood.*

NAME

signs and symbols Everywhere

What do these signs and symbols mean?

Signs pack a lot of information into a very small space.
We quickly learn the meanings of symbols and recognise the shapes of traffic signs.

Create signs for the following (think about what shapes and colours might work best).

Low-flying pigeons	No pedestrians
Thinking allowed in here	Silence

Make up your own signs and symbols.

Visual Literacy: *interpreting and creating symbols and signs.*

NAME

MISSING STEPS

The illustrator has gone to tea. Put in the missing steps for these drawings.

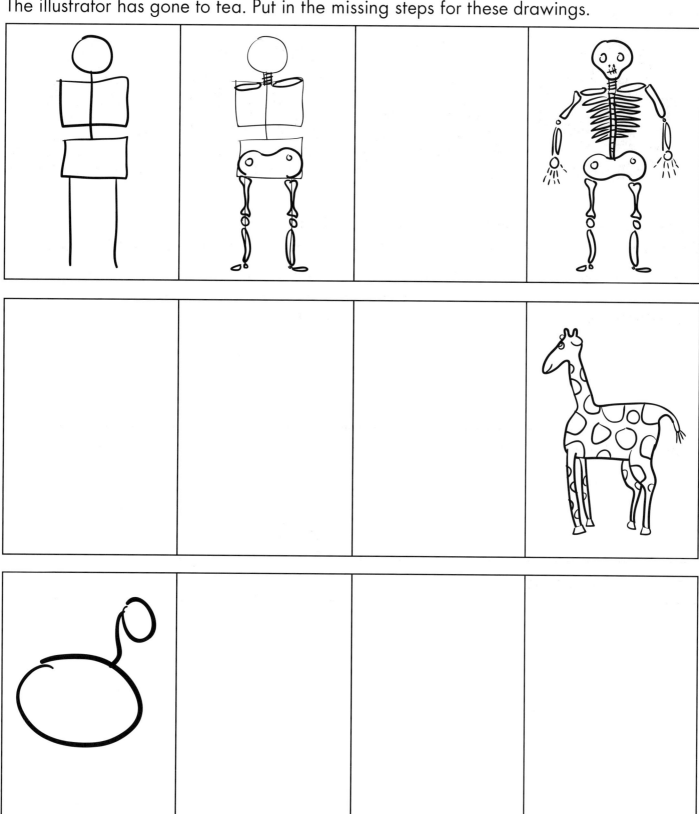

Visual Literacy: *using shape and proportion to create a drawing sequence.*

NAME

Don't Do It!

Why do we do things our friends ask us to, even when we know we shouldn't?

_____

_____

_____

Does it matter if someone says you are chicken? _____

Make a cartoon strip to show a situation that puts a child under pressure to do something they shouldn't. Show what they can do to resist the pressure.

Values: _dealing with peer pressure._

NAME

But I only told one friend

Should you tell your secrets to a friend?

_____

_____

Who can you trust to keep a secret?

_____

_____

_____

_____

When someone tells you a secret, what should you do and why?

_____

_____

_____

_____

Is it ever okay to tell someone's secrets? Explain.

_____

_____

_____

_____

_____

_____

Values: _considering the needs of others._

NAME

My Poor Dog

My dog's got to be put to sleep!

That's cruel.

Mum says it's too old now.

What do you think? Should a pet be put to sleep?

Agree because ...	Disagree because ...
Reason 1	Reason 1
Reason 2	Reason 2
Reason 3	Reason 3
Reason 4	Reason 4
Reason 5	Reason 5

Values: *considering different perspectives.*

REALITY TV

NAME

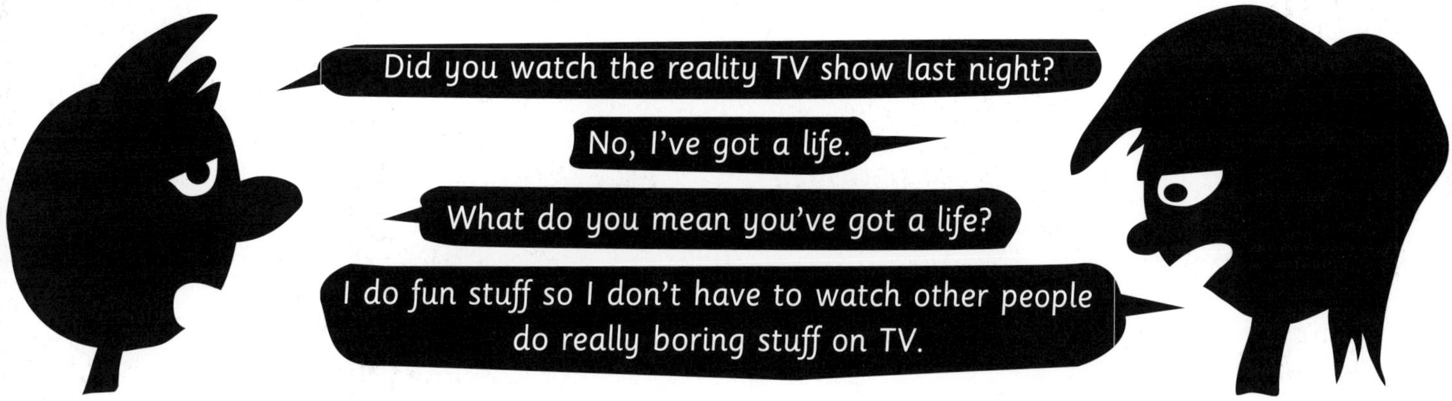

Did you watch the reality TV show last night?

No, I've got a life.

What do you mean you've got a life?

I do fun stuff so I don't have to watch other people do really boring stuff on TV.

Why do people like reality TV?

_____

_____

Can you learn anything useful or interesting from reality TV?

_____

Does reality TV help you with your friends?

_____

What would be more fun and better for your friendships than watching reality TV?

_____

_____

_____

Show some fun things you can do by yourself or with friends.

Values: *reflecting on the choices we make.*

NAME

SHOW OFF

There is a time to show off. **There is a time not to show off.**

I completed my certificate in self-defence last night.

I got a new mobile phone on Saturday.

It is okay to show off about something that you worked hard for to achieve.

It is not okay to show off about things that you have that others do not.

If you want to show off then think about something you are good at now that you couldn't do before.

Last year I wanted to be able to _____

_____

But I couldn't because I _____

_____

My goal was to _____

Now I _____

because (list the steps you take to master something new) ...

Step 1
Step 2
Step 3
Step 4

Share your accomplishment with some friends.

Values: *sharing goals and stories of perseverance.*

NAME

FARMYARD MUSIC

Country music usually tells a very tuneful story and often has a chorus.

Farmyard music tells a tuneful story too.

For your farmyard music, create a farmyard band made up of animal noises.

List the noises

Animals	Animal Noises

Create a short story-line to be sung.

_____

_____

_____

_____

Make up a chorus.

_____

_____

Find a way of writing the musical score using symbols for the noises. The class can be the farmyard band as you sing the song.

Music: *creating rhythm and a tune to accompany a simple song.*

SOUND SCAPE

RUNS THROUGH TIDAL WAVES

NAME

Roaring waves–sand in a can; Splashing–hands in water

It was a dark, stormy night as we sat on a sheltered bench eating fish and chips.

An owl hooted in the distance and footsteps approached. We dropped our fish and chips and ran towards the busy road for safety.

A sound scape tells a story using only noises and sound effects. Your job is to identify the noises that you would have heard sitting on that bench and tell the story using only sounds.

List your thoughts and ideas (for example, the owl was in the distance so a quiet hoot is needed) and how you will make the sounds.

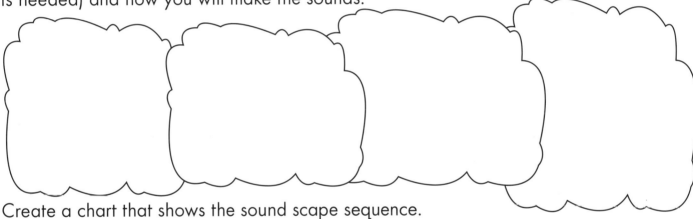

Create a chart that shows the sound scape sequence.

You can experiment with available objects in the classroom. Also make sounds with your voices and bodies to get the message across.

Sounds							

Rehearse, and then record (on an audio cassette recorder) and present it to the class. Can the class identify how you made some of the noises?

Music: creating sound effects and sequences to tell a story.

NAME

Stress Buster Bustle

Stand tall and tense, turn to jelly

Wobble, wobble, slowly set, stand tall and tense.

To the tune of "Wheels on the Bus"

The people at the dance go tense, tense, tense... all day long,

followed by "turn to jelly" and then "slowly set".

The "Stress Buster Bustle" is a new dance craze designed to release stress, loosen people up and make them feel happy.

The problem is that it hasn't been invented yet. That's your job.

You need to:

• Choose some music.

• Create a sequence of stress release actions that include stretches, flexes and loosening up actions.

• Rehearse and present your new dance craze.

• Evaluate your music choice and dance. Did they work? Why/why not?

Music and Dance: *creating movement sequences matched to purpose and music.*

NAME

All Do the New Hokey Cokey

Do the stamp
and shake it.

Put your left blink on
Put your left blink off.

Choose a song and dance that you know well.
Write new words and create new actions for it.

Rehearse, present it, and then get your audience up and doing it.

Music and Dance: *innovating on a dance and song.*

NAME

Wanted

A nine-letter word that:

- is a noun
- is a compound word
- is the name of an object that people take to the beach
- begins with s
- where the second part of the word is 'board'.

Reward

Another compound word to play

Find some compound words of your own. Create and list clues from hardest and least helpful to easiest and most helpful, and make a wanted poster for the one you like best.

Wanted

Reward

Wanted

Reward

Wanted

Reward

Find out how many clues you will read before the class guesses your word?

Communication: *extending vocabulary and grammatical understanding.*

NAME

GOOD FOOD JUST GOT BETTER

Giving a recipe a fancy name makes something everyday and boring somehow more attractive. Presentation is everything, especially when accompanied by attractive descriptions.

Sausage, mash, peas
and gravy £5.95

Finest sausages on a bed of
greens, trickled with jus £15.95

What would you do to make the
following boring dishes appealing?

Fried rice and chicken	Jelly and ice-cream	Fish and chips

How would you revamp your favourite meal?

Communication: *understanding persuasive techniques.*

NAME

Guess What's in My Mind

I really like Chinese...

Food

No writing – it looks so neat.

Did you know that people only half listen. A lot of the time they think they know what someone is going to say, so they cut them off or finish their sentences for them.

But can you read what is in people's minds?

You are going to ask four people whether they think school uniforms are a good idea, and tell you why or why not. Make sure you listen carefully and do not cut the speaker off. Before you do though, create a thought bubble for each of the people showing what you think they will say.

Teacher	Friend 1
Friend 2	**Friend 3**

So how well did you second guess? Comment here on any surprises and on how close you second guessed.

_____

_____

_____

_____

Communication: *listening carefully and with a purpose.*

NAME

Over to You, Channel 42

Write the script for an on-the-scene TV report.

Include

Who you are.

Where you are.

What you are reporting about.

What you have found out.

An interview with an onlooker

Question 1

Answer 1

Question 2

Answer 2

Sign off.

Communication: *creating a live TV report.*

RUMBUSTICAL

NAME

You are so rumbustical.

Why did she say that?

R is 1, U is 2, M is 3, like that. It's our secret code.

Hmm!

If the letter is not in the code then you use the letter because it has no number.

What does this secret message mean?

11 E 7 6   W 1 8 7 E   6 E 9 1 E 7   3 E 6 6 10 G E 6

What secret message could you write?

Choose another word and make a code. Try it out.
Keep trying if your first one does not work.

Communicate with your friends, choosing a different word each time.

Can you unlock a message without the code?

If you can, your word was not good enough.

Communication: *creating verbal codes.*

The Perfect Character

I wish I had straight hair.

I wish I didn't have to wear glasses.

Why do people always wish they were different.

Invent four cartoon characters (two goodies and two baddies).

Give them some special characteristics (at least one you like and one you do not).

Show what they think about their characteristics.

Write on the lines what they think of each other.

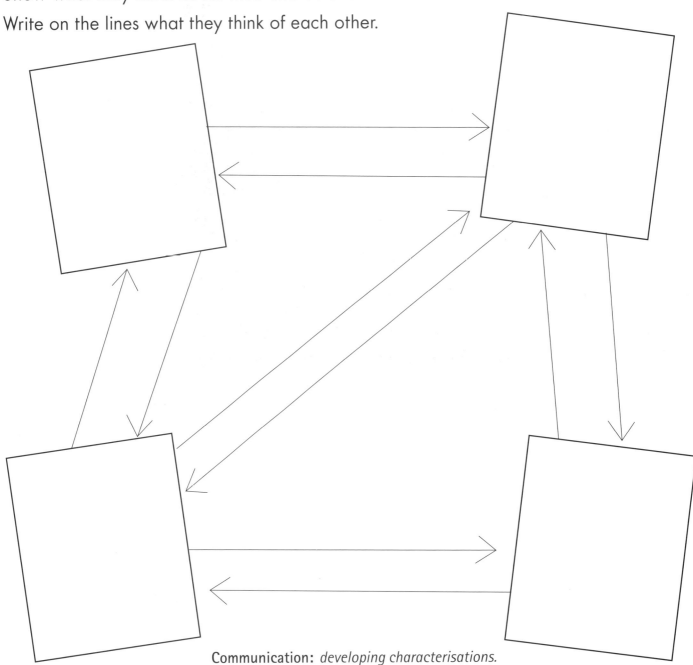

Communication: *developing characterisations.*

CHALLENGES

 **TASK CARD 1**

How to Have No Friends

What you need:

- bag of lollies
- some nasty comments
- a bad habit
- 3 or 4 friends

What to do:

Act out this skit with some friends.

Eat some lollies but DO NOT share.

Make some nasty comments.

Carry out your bad habit (e.g. pick your nails).

Watch as your friends walk away.

With your friends, rewrite the script to show what to do to have some friends. Act it out.

 **TASK CARD 2**

Hum, Humming a Round

What you need:

- 2 or 3 friends

What to do:

Choose a song that you know really well.

Practise humming it until you are good at it.

Try to get everyone humming in a different pitch. You could add humour by having a very high and a very low hummer.

Split the song up so that you all start at a different time.

You will either hold the last note so that you all finish together or you may need a couple of twiddly bits at the end.

Add some actions.

Perform it to the class.

TASK CARD 3 — Hunters

What you need:

- a magnifying glass
- pencil and paper

What to do:

You will look really closely at some parts of familiar objects, perhaps at an unusual angle to them.

Draw what you see through the magnifying glass.

Make several drawings and then swap with a friend.

Go on a hunt now for objects that you can see better by enlarging or from an unusual viewpoint.

TASK CARD 4 — Make a Scene

What you need:

- pencil and paper
- coloured pens or crayons
- magazine
- scissors
- glue

What to do:

Cut out a picture of an object from a magazine (we cut out a Nike shoe).

Change the scale of the shoe; make it really large or really tiny in proportion to the things that you draw into the scene around it.

Add colour and emotion to your scene.

Picaria

What you need:

- pencil and paper
- 6 counters (three of each colour)

What to do:

Play "Picaria" as it was played by the Spanish conquistadors.

Players take turns to place one of their counters onto the board but not onto the middle dot.

Players can then move one space in any direction on their turn (including onto the middle dot).

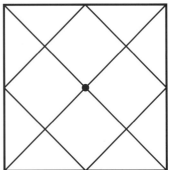

The first player to get three in a row, diagonally, horizontally or vertically is the winner.

Now ask some "what ifs": what if we used 4 counters each? What if we grew the board? Experiment and invent a new version of the game.

Hook Your Audience

What you need:

- pencil and paper
- some friends

What to do:

Ask each of your friends to write a really boring introduction for a story. Some really boring sentences are:

It was night-time.
The cat sat on the mat.

Everyone then works on the same sentences, trying to make them interesting so that a reader would want to read on. The original words have to be kept in the same order in the new sentences.

Really interesting sentences are:

It was night-time, the moon was full and a howling broke
through the eerie sky.
The grinning tabby cat sat patiently on the mat, watching the
household, flexing his claws in anticipation.

Rate each new sentence out of 5 and say why.
Total the scores to find which sentences rate the best.